SUSSEX

Halswood

Published by Halswood Stationers

Copyright © Halswood Stationers
Image copyright © Iain McGowan 2010

British Library Cataloguing-in-Publication Data
A CIP record for this title is available from the
British Library

ISBN 978 0 85717 009 5

HALSWOOD STATIONERS
Halsgrove House,
Ryelands Industrial Estate,
Bagley Road, Wellington, Somerset TA21 9PZ
Tel: 01823 653777   Fax: 01823 216796
email: sales@halsgrove.com

Part of the Halsgrove group of companies
Information on all Halsgrove titles is available at:
www.halsgrove.com

Printed and bound in China by
Toppan Leefung Printing Ltd (0)

Front cover: The Seven Sisters from Seaford Head.

Back cover: The fifteenth-century manor of Great
Dixter near Northiam.

Title page: Beachy Head.

Overleaf: The Royal Pavilion, Brighton.

Oilseed rape fields on the slopes of Bury Hill.

INTRODUCTION

Sussex is possibly the best known of all seaside counties and contains a remarkable variety of features and scenery within its 120km breadth from Thorney to Camber. Often described as the most English of counties, Sussex can almost be defined by the fresh salty tag of the sea air, and the soft, gentle expanse and wide views of the South Downs or of the distant Weald.

There are many who would say that Sussex has it all; from the busy, sunny promenades and elegant terraces of Brighton and Eastbourne to the drama of the white chalk cliffs of the Seven Sisters; from the dusty, homely flint Downland villages to the medieval hammer ponds lying still and silent in the depths of the Wealden valleys. Sussex attracts enormous crowds to its seaside resorts in summer when often the Downs are dotted with more walkers and cyclists than the once ubiquitous South Downs sheep. Yet there are places where one can still steal away for solitude, amongst the deep, sunken lanes and tracks of the hill country around Midhurst and Petworth or the rifes of the Manhood Peninsula.

It is a county of tremendous, yet harmonious contrasts, a county of inexhaustible richness in both its heritage and physical geography. Iain McGowan, the internationally-renowned landscape photographer, based in Sussex where his roots have run deep since early childhood, carries on the great tradition of artists who have been stimulated by the area: through his lens he captures the essential beauty and character of Sussex.

Address books tend to be well used and have a long life. Along with important contact details, they keep track of the user's friends and acquaintances, tracing their lives over time and from place to place. And, if properly attended to, an address book eventually becomes a journal in itself, and an attractive and permanent keepsake. Whether bought as a gift or for personal use, this *Sussex Address Book*, with its superb pictorial reminders of the county, will provide years of pleasure.

USEFUL ADDRESSES AND TELEPHONE NUMBERS

A

Old Town, Hastings.

A

Clearing skies, Worthing. The beach, totally devoid of any visitors,
slowly dries out after a night's rain. Worthing Pier is in the background.

B

Early morning light, Dell Quay.

B

B

B

Winter snow on Bignor Hill.

C

_____
_____
_____
_____
_____
_____
_____
_____
_____
_____
_____
_____
_____
_____
_____
_____
_____
_____
_____
_____
_____
_____
_____

The colourful gardens of Southover Grange.

C

C

C

Charleston Farm. Often known as Bloomsbury in Sussex, the seventeenth-century Charleston Farm was the home of the painters Clive and Vanessa Bell and Duncan Grant from about 1916 onwards.

D

Brunswick Terrace, Hove

D

D

D

Morning reflections, Bodiam Castle.

The Royal Military Canal near Iden.

E

E

E

Bosham from across Bosham channel.

F

Nymans Gardens at Handcross, not far from Crawley.

F

F

F

Rye Harbour.

G

A glorious spring day on the Downs near Firle Beacon
looking inland towards Charleston Farm and Kipling's
'wooded dim blue goodness of the Weald'.

G

G

G

The Seven Sisters from Seaford Head.

H

Church Street, Steyning.

H

H

H

The timber-framed Priest House at West Hoathley.

Church Square, Rye.

I

J

A view of Arundel Castle from the banks of the
River Arun on a cold, misty winter's morning.

J

Ashdown Forest.

K

The Bluebell Railway.

K

L

A misty, early October morning view from
Bury Hill looking down to the Arun valley.

L

L

L

A view over the Rother Levels near Iden looking
towards the Kent border and the Isle of Oxney.

The west front of Petworth House in its parkland setting was
built during the last years of the seventeenth century.

M

M

M

Wakehurst Place.

N

Lancing College Chapel.

O

o

The Long Man of Wilmington.

O

'Underhill lane' near Alciston.

The eleventh-century church of St Mary, Chithurst, stands on a knoll,
possibly a pre-Christian site, above the banks of the River Rother.

PQ

Hammer pond near Horsted Keynes.

Lower Promenade, Brighton.

R

A late winter's afternoon at Chanctonbury Ring.

Normans Bay.

S

S

S

Buildings in St Anne's Hill, Lewes.

The Fifteenth Century Bookshop

The fifteenth-century manor of Great Dixter near Northiam.

T

Cricket at Chichester.

UV

Summer skies and poppies. Looking across open fields to the Trundle.

UV

Standen House near East Grinstead.

Pagham Rife in early summer.

W

Sunset over Pagham Harbour.

The Causeway, Horsham.

XYZ